Date ..../........../..........

Number Puzzle

- The sum of two numbers is 63.
- The two numbers are in the ratio 3 : 4.

Can you work out what the numbers are?

This diagram may help you.

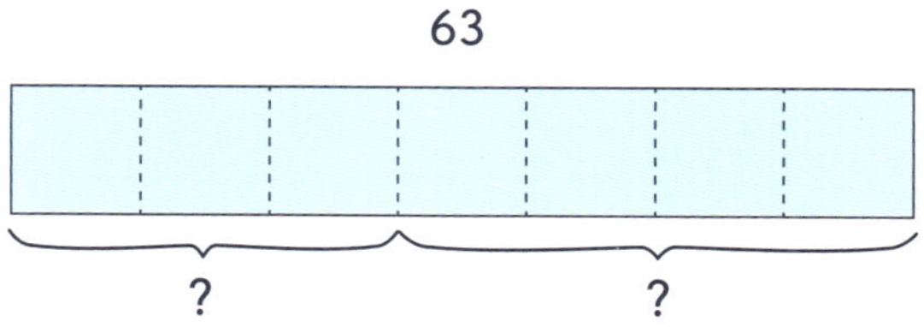

Teacher notes

Have ready: calculator

Date ..../........../..........

Making Chutney

Here is a recipe for some apple chutney. It makes enough for four 500 g jars. You only want to make 1 jar, and so use only $\frac{1}{4}$ of the recipe.

How much of each ingredient do you need?

Apple Chutney

1 kg cooking apples, peeled and chopped into small chunks

5 eating apples, peeled and chopped into large chunks

2 large onions, sliced

3 tsp fresh root ginger, finely chopped

1 tsp peppercorns

500 g granulated sugar

250 ml vinegar

Teacher notes

Have ready: calculator

Date ..../........../..........

Fraction and Decimal Equivalents

0·1666666

The decimal in the star is the decimal equivalent of a unit fraction (the numerator is 1).

Using your knowledge of common fraction equivalents and trial and improvement, can you work out what unit fraction this represents? You can use a calculator to help.

Can you think of 2 fractions that could be added together to make the decimal in the star?

Teacher notes

Date ..../........../..........

Equal Steps

0	?	?	?	?	?	?	?	96

In this sequence there are seven numbers missing between 0 and 96, with equal steps between them.

Can you work out what the numbers are?

What if there had been fifteen numbers between 0 and 96?

Can you work out what those numbers would have been?

Teacher notes

Date ..../........../..........

Perimeter Patterns

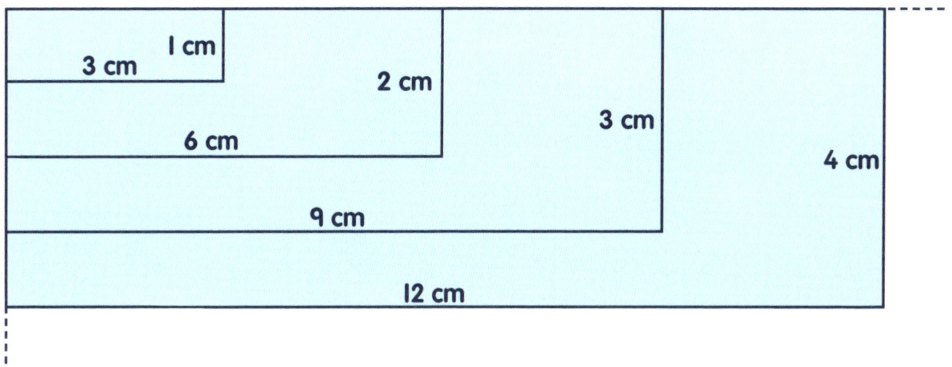

The perimeters of this series of rectangles are 8 cm, 16 cm, 24 cm and so on.

Can you say what the perimeter of the 12th rectangle in the series will be?

Can you work out what the perimeter of the nth rectangle will be?

Teacher notes

Date ..../........../..........

Paddling Pool

You want to fill a paddling pool with water.

Your bucket holds 7·25 ℓ of water and it takes 16 full buckets to fill up the pool.

How much water will there be in the paddling pool once it is full?

After lots of splashing, the level of the water has gone down.

You add another 9 full buckets of water to fill it up again.

How much more water have you added?

Teacher notes

Have ready: Numicon 2–9 Numeral Cards

Date ..../........../..........

Missing Number Clues

This calculation contains all the digits from 2 to 9 once only.

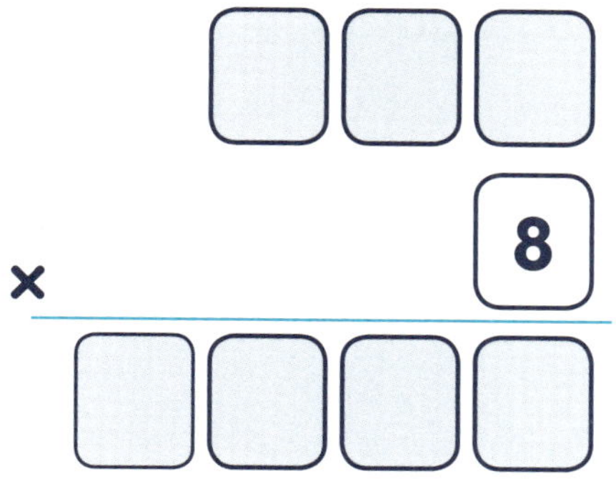

Can you use the clues below to work out the complete calculation? One number has been given for you. You could lay out the Numicon Numeral Cards 2–9 face up and turn over the cards once you have used them.

Clues:

- The tens and units digits of the **product** are multiples of 3.
- In the 3-digit number, the units digit is even and the rest are odd.

Teacher notes

Date ..../........../..........

Sharing Prizes

A team won £322 in a treasure hunt. They got £14 each when they shared the prize equally between them. Can you work out how many people were in the group?

Another team of 26 people took part in the treasure hunt and won £156·78 between them. Can you find how much they would get each if they shared the prize equally?

Teacher notes

Date ..../........../..........

Lifeboat Capacity

A cruise ship carries lifeboats and life rafts in case of emergency.

A lifeboat can carry a total mass of no more than 11 250 kg.

A life raft is designed to carry up to 37 people.

The cruise ship has the same number of lifeboats as life rafts.

The cruise ship carries 2018 passengers and 600 crew members.

How many lifeboats and life rafts should be on the ship so that there are enough to rescue everyone safely when the ship is at full capacity? Assume an average mass of 75 kg per person.

Teacher notes

Date ..../........../..........

Fraction Designs

Here is a design. What fraction of the whole shape is shaded blue?

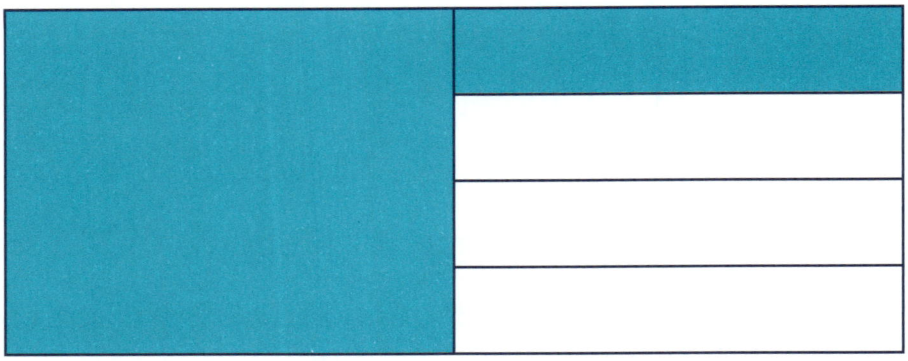

What about this square design? What fraction of the whole square is unshaded?

Teacher notes

Date ..../........../..........

What Could the Fractions be?

Two fractions add to make $1\frac{5}{6}$. What could the fractions be? How many possible combinations can you find?

$$? + ? = 1\frac{5}{6}$$

The difference between two fractions is $\frac{1}{2}$. What could the fractions be? How many possible combinations can you find?

$$? - ? = \frac{1}{2}$$

Teacher notes

Date ..../........../..........

Vegetable Patch

Alia has a rectangular vegetable patch. She plants $\frac{1}{2}$ of it with carrots. When they have grown she pulls up $\frac{2}{3}$ of them.

What fraction of the whole vegetable patch has she pulled up?

You can use this diagram to help you.

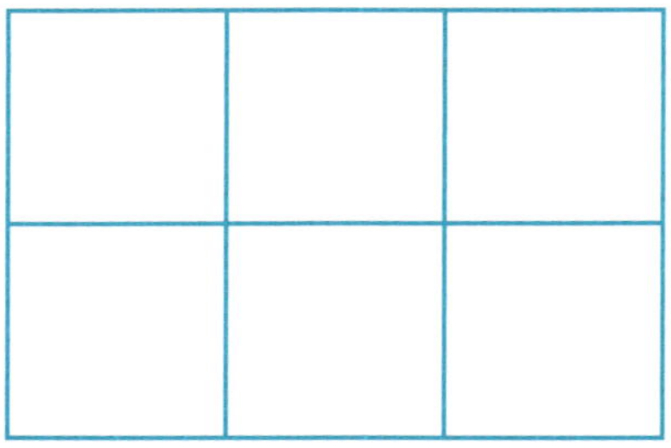

Teacher notes

Date ..../........../..........

Fraction Machines

Here are some inputs and outputs of 2 function machines, jumbled up.
Can you work out what the function is for each machine?

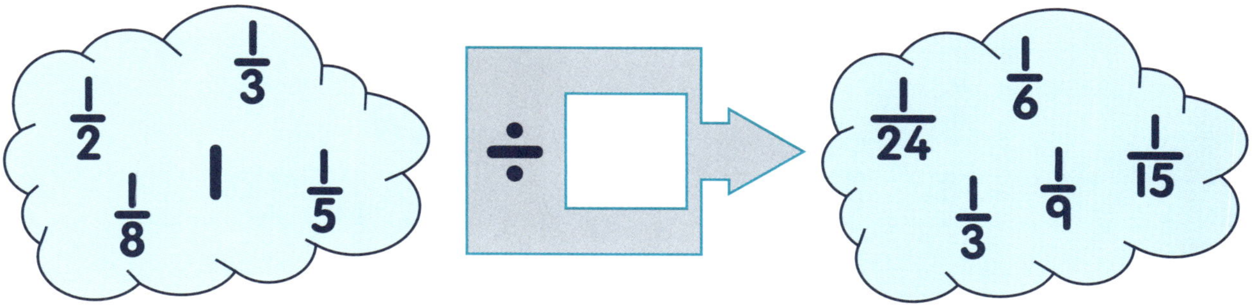

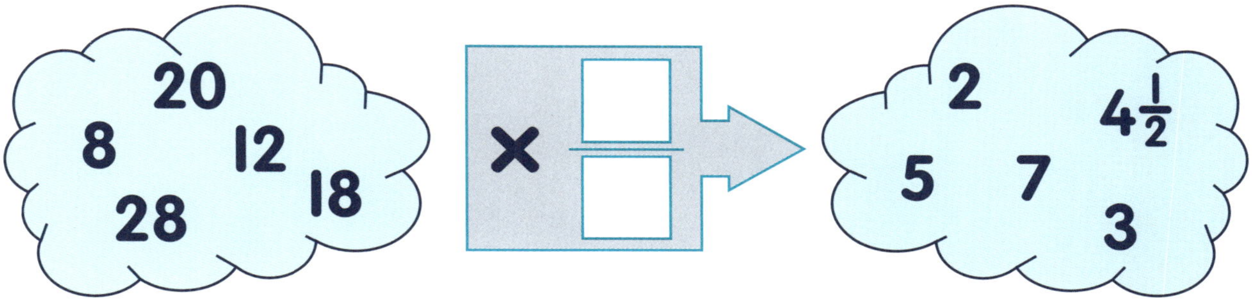

Teacher notes

Date ..../........../..........

Shape Values

In this grid each shape has a different value. The number at the end of a row shows the sum of the values in that row.

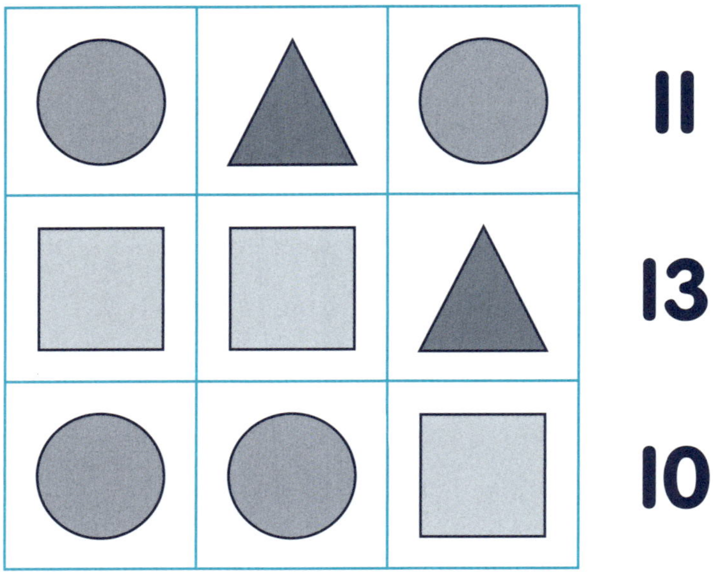

Can you work out the value of each shape?

Teacher notes

Date ..../........../..........

Leg Count

A farmer keeps chickens and cows in the same field. Altogether there are 30 animals and they have 74 legs.

How many are cows and how many are chickens?

Teacher notes

Have ready: extra paper

Date ..../........./.........

Car Wash Earnings

On average, a hand car wash company cleans 24 vehicles a day. Of these, $\frac{1}{3}$ are vans or 4x4s, all of which have an inside and outside clean. The remainder are cars, $\frac{3}{4}$ of which have an outside wash only.

Outside Wash Only

✔ Hand wash and dry
✔ Wheels cleaned

Cars **£7·50** Vans and 4x4s **£10·75**

Inside and Outside

✔ Full outside wash
✔ Vacuum seats, carpet and boot

Cars **£12·15** Vans and 4x4s **£14·99**

Can you work out how much money the hand car wash company earns in a week, on average?

How much does the company earn in a year, on average?

Teacher notes

Date ..../........../..........

What are the Numbers?

The sum of two numbers is 393 and the difference between those two numbers is 79.

Can you work out what the two numbers are?

Teacher notes

Have ready: extra paper

Date ..../........../..........

Function Machines

Leo made a function machine that gives the following input and output:

What are the different 1-step functions that might be in the machine?

What if it is a 2-step function? What could some of those functions be?

What if Leo's machine also does:

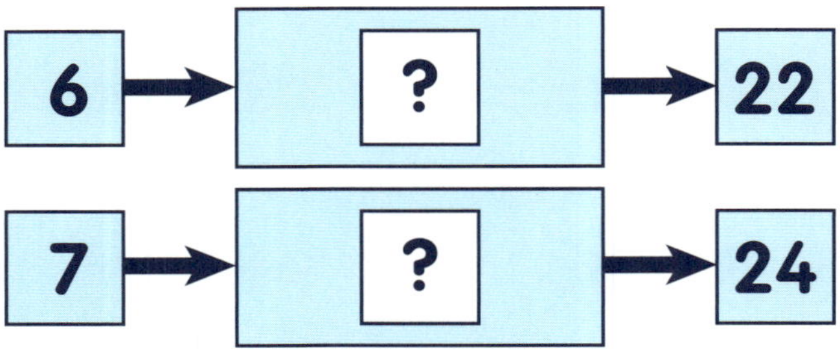

What do you think the function is? Is it a 1-step or a 2-step function?

Teacher notes

Date ..../........../..........

Mini-Marathon

Freya is training for a mini-marathon. She wants to calculate how many calories to eat to replace all the energy she will use as she runs. She knows that someone her age uses 10 calories per hour for every kilogram of their weight, running at a steady pace.

Freya weighs 36 kg and she runs for half an hour every day after school. How many calories will she use in a week?

Freya's friends would like to do the run too, and want to know how to make this calculation for each of their weights. How could Freya write her calculation for them, if A = calories burned per hour and B = weight in kg?

Teacher notes

My Learning Log

Date ..../........../..........

I know how to…

Date ..../........../..........

I know these facts:

Date ..../........../..........

I can use maths in everyday life when...

Date ..../........../..........

Reflections.

My favourite maths was...

I would like more time to think about...

I felt proud when...

numicon®

Number, Pattern and Calculating

Explorer 6b

Progress Book

Can you write in the missing ratio of water and sand?

Your **Explorer Progress Book 6b** contains:

- Fun activities that give you a chance to show what you understand and what you are thinking.
- Learning Logs where you can record what you know and what you can do.

Say what your favourite piece of work was.

Say what you need more time to think about.

Say what you were most proud of.

Information for your teacher

The activities in this book match the activity groups in the Teaching Resource Handbook for Number, Pattern and Calculating 6. In the top right-hand corner of each page, you can see which activity group it matches.

A range of apparatus should be freely available to children as they work on the activities. The 'Have ready' box at the top of the page shows specific resource requirements where appropriate.

Use the 'Teacher notes' section of each page to give children feedback.

OXFORD
UNIVERSITY PRESS

Great Clarendon Street, Oxford, OX2 6DP, United Kingdom

Oxford University Press is a department of the University of Oxford. It furthers the University's objective of excellence in research, scholarship, and education by publishing worldwide. Oxford is a registered trade mark of Oxford University Press in the UK and in certain other countries

Text and illustrations
© Oxford University Press 2016

Typeset by Phoenix Photosetting, Chatham
Figurative artworks by Adrian Barclay
Technical artworks by Phoenix Photosetting, Chatham
Cover artwork by David Semple
Written by Jayne Campling, Adella Osborne and Dr Tony Wing

The moral rights of the authors have been asserted.

This edition published 2016

All rights reserved. No part of this publication may be reproduced, stored in a retrieval system, or transmitted, in any form or by any means, without the prior permission in writing of Oxford University Press, or as expressly permitted by law, by licence or under terms agreed with the appropriate reprographics rights organization. Enquiries concerning reproduction outside the scope of the above should be sent to the Rights Department, Oxford University Press, at the address above.

You must not circulate this work in any other form and you must impose this same condition on any acquirer

ISBN 978-0-19-830507-1

3 5 7 9 10 8 6 4 2

Printed in China by Golden Cup

Oxford OWL
Discover eBooks, inspirational resources, advice and support
www.oxfordowl.co.uk

OXFORD
UNIVERSITY PRESS

How to get in touch:
web www.oxfordprimary.co.uk
email primary.enquiries@oup.com
tel. +44 (0) 1536 452610
fax +44 (0) 1865 313472

ISBN 978-0-19-830507-1
9 780198 305071

numicon

Number, Pattern and Calculating

Explorer 6b
Progress Book

Name .... Class ....

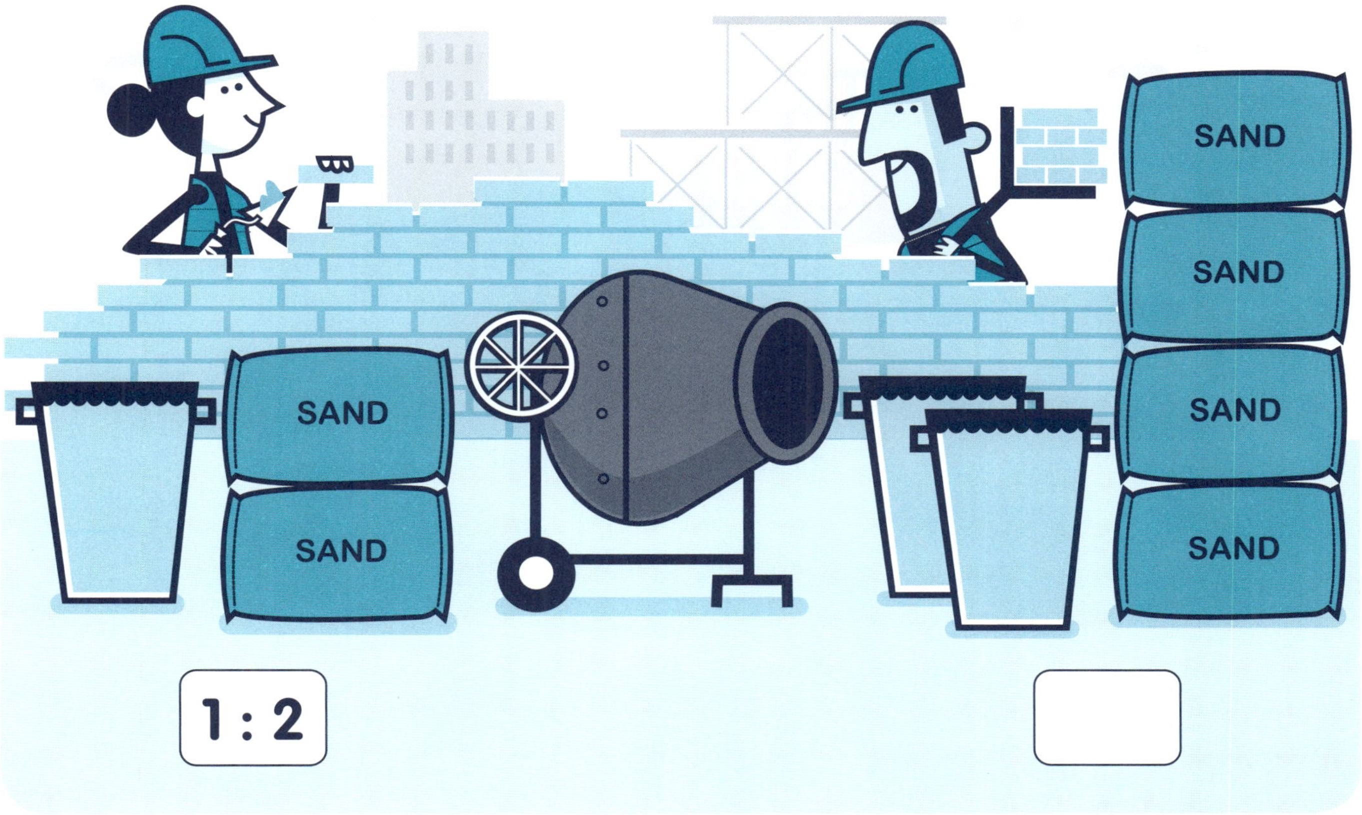

OXFORD

Have ready: ruler

Date ..../........../..........

Classroom Floor Plan

Nicolai drew an accurate floor plan of his classroom.

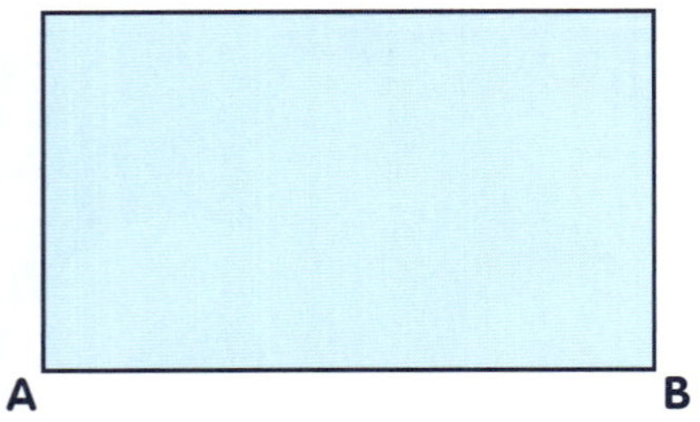

Scale: 1 : 300 cm

Measure Nicolai's floor plan. How long is his classroom in the real world?

Teacher notes